Moto GP Trivia Quiz Book

500 Questions on The Titans of the Track

Chris Bradshaw

For rights and permissions, please contact:
C_D_Bradshaw@hotmail.com

ISBN-13: 978-1-7392137-1-8

This book is unofficial and not authorised by MotoGP.

Front cover image created by headfuzz by grimboid. Check out his great collection of TV, movie and sport-themed posters online at:

https://www.etsy.com/shop/headfuzzbygrimboid

Introduction

Think you know about the MotoGP? Put your knowledge to the test with this collection of quizzes on the titans of the track.

The book covers the whole history of the motorcycle Grand Prix world championship, from the earliest races on to the wild 1970s and 80s through to the present day.

The biggest names in racing history are present and correct so look out for questions on Valentino Rossi, Marc Marquez, Mick Doohan, Barry Sheene, Francesco Bagnaia and many, many more.

There are 500 questions in all covering teams and riders, circuits and strategy and much else besides.

Each quiz contains a selection of 20 questions and is either a mixed bag of pot luck testers or is centred on a specific category such as MotoGP Legends or Memorable Moments.

There are easy, medium and hard questions offering something for MotoGP novices as well as professors of Grand Prix history.

You'll find the answers to each quiz below the bottom of the following quiz. For example, the answers to Quiz 1: Pot Luck, are underneath Quiz 2: 2022 Season. The only exception is Quiz 25: Pot Luck. The answers to these can be found under the Quiz 1 questions.

All questions relate to premier class races unless otherwise stated. Records are accurate to the start of the 2023 season and once again, refer to premier class races only unless stated otherwise.

We hope you enjoy the MotoGP Trivia Quiz Book.

About the Author

Chris Bradshaw has written more than 30 quiz books including titles for Britain's biggest selling daily newspaper, The Sun, and The Times (of London). In addition to the NFL, he has written extensively on Formula One, soccer, cricket, darts and poker.

He lives in Birmingham, England and has been following motorsport for over 30 years.

Acknowledgements

Many thanks to Ken and Veronica Bradshaw, Heidi Grant, Steph, James, Ben and Will Roe and Graham Nash.

CONTENTS

Moments

Quiz 1: Pot Luck

1. How many points does the winner of a MotoGP race earn?

2. On what day of the week does a main MotoGP Grand Prix race usually take place?

3. Which venue hosted the British Grand Prix from 1987 through to 2009?

4. How many riders receive points in a MotoGP race?

5. In 1987, who became the first Aussie to be crowned World Champion?

6. Which Italian star won 13 races between 1998 and 2005 but was never crowned World Champion?

7. Which of the two Binder brothers is older – Brad or Darryn?

8. What flag is waved at the first rider to cross the finish line in a MotoGP race?

9. Riders from which country have won the most races in the history of MotoGP?

10. Which country is second on that list of most MotoGP wins?

11. Which Spanish rider made his debut in 1992 but didn't win his first World Championship until 1999?

12. Who is the only World Champion whose first name and surname start with the same letter?

13. What colour flag does a marshal wave to inform riders that the track is clear and ready to use?

14. Which constructor announced in July 2022 that it was leaving MotoGP?

15. All tyres on MotoGP bikes are supplied by which manufacturer?

16. What was the only bike manufacturer that failed to secure a victory during the 2022 MotoGP season?

17. Which Grand Prix was hosted at the İzmit Körfez Circuit from 2005 to 2007?

18. Which Japanese rider started 124 consecutive races between 2001 and 2008?

19. What is the engine capacity of a MotoGP bike? a) 500cc b) 750cc c) 1,000cc

20. In what year was the sport officially rebranded MotoGP? a) 2001 b) 2002 c) 2003

Quiz 25: Answers

1. Kenny Roberts Sr 2. Johann Zarco 3. Casey Stoner and Francesco Bagnaia 4. Max Biaggi 5. Australian Grand Prix 6. John Surtees 7. Clockwise 8. Two 9. Sweden 10. Formula One cars 11. Austria 12. True 13. Three 14. Valentino Rossi 15. Mick Doohan 16. Casey Stoner 17. Marc Marquez 18. Estoril 19. a) 22 litres 20. a) Florence

Quiz 2: 2022 Season

1. Which Italian won the 2022 MotoGP World Championship?

2. He won that title riding for which team?

3. The 2022 season started with which Asian-hosted race?

4. Who won the 2022 British MotoGP?

5. The 2022 MotoGP season featured how many different teams?

6. Who won the team competition in 2022?

7. Who were the two Spaniards to win races during the 2022 season?

8. Three former MotoGP World Champions appeared in races during the 2022 season. Which three?

9. Who won the 2022 Constructors' Championship?

10. True or false – 10 different riders held pole position during the 2022 season?

11. After amassing 111 points, who was named Rookie of the Year for the 2022 season?

12. Who gained pole position on five occasions in 2022 but didn't go on to win a race?

13. Who was the top Independent MotoGP Team Rider for the 2022 season?

14. Which country had the most riders during the 2022 season? (clue: There were 10 from this country)

15. Attracting a raceday crowd of 110,103 what was the best attended race in the 2022 MotoGP season?

16. With just 6,605 spectators, what was the worst attended race of 2022?

17. Riders from how many different countries took part in the 2022 MotoGP season?

18. The 2022 season was made up of how many races?

19. How many different riders won a Grand Prix during the 2022 season? a) five b) six c) seven

20. How many points did the winning rider gain to secure the 2022 World Championship? a) 255 b) 265 c) 275

Quiz 1: Answers

1. 25 points 2. Sunday 3. Donington 4. 15 riders 5. Wayne Gardner 6. Max Biaggi 7. Brad 8. Chequered flag 9. Italy 10. Spain 11. Àlex Crivillé 12. Marc Marquez 13. Green 14. Suzuki 15. Michelin 16. Honda 17. Turkish 18. Shinya Nakano 19. c) 1,000cc 20. b) 2002

Quiz 3: Pot Luck

1. Who are the only father and son duo to have both won the World Championship?

2. FIM are the initials of the global governing body of motorcycle racing. What do those initials stand for?

3. The headquarters of FIM are located in which country?

4. Which rookie crashed a record 27 times throughout the 2022 season?

5. Who holds the record for the most premier class race wins by an American rider?

6. What was the only South American country to host a race during the 2022 Moto GP season?

7. True or false – Up to 1976, the Isle of Man TT formed the British leg of the World Championship?

8. In 1983, who became the first 21-year-old to be crowned World Champion?

9. The runner-up in a MotoGP race is awarded how many points?

10. In 1974, Edmund Czihak became the first, and so far, only, Grand Prix winner from which country?

11. Who was crowned World Champion for the first time in 2020?

12. How many races did he win in that championship-winning season?

13. On what day of the week do MotoGP Sprint Races usually take place?

14. Of all the riders to take part in the 2022 MotoGP, what characteristic was shared by just Johann Zarco and Enea Bastianini?

15. Who holds the record for the most wins in the history of the Australian Grand Prix?

16. Who was the only German rider to win points in 2022?

17. Who holds the record for the most race wins in a rookie MotoGP season?

18. How many races did he win to set that record?

19. How long does a MotoGP usually take (approximately)? a) 30 minutes b) 45 minutes c) 60 minutes

20. Jorge Lorenzo was born on which Spanish island? a) Ibiza b) Majorca c) Lanzarote

Quiz 2: Answers

1. Francesco Bagnaia 2. Ducati Lenovo Team 3. Qatar MotoGP 4. Francesco Bagnaia 5. 12 teams 6. Ducati Lenovo 7. Aleix Espargaró and Alex Rins 8. Fabio Quartararo, Joan Mir and Marc Marquez 9. Ducati 10. True 11. Marco Bezzecchi 12. Jorge Martin 13. Enea Bastianini 14. Italy 15. French MotoGP at Le Mans 16. Qatar MotoGP 17. Nine 18. 20 races 19. c) Seven 20. b) 265 points

Quiz 4: Valentino Rossi

1. What nationality is Rossi?

2. Rossi was crowned premier class World Champion on how many occasions?

3. True or false – Rossi crashed out of his first two premier class races?

4. Throughout the whole of his career, Rossi rode what number bike?

5. In what position did Rossi finish in his first season in the 500cc World Championship?

6. Rossi claimed his first Grand Prix in 2000, winning which race?

7. Which race did Rossi win a record eight times between 2002 and 2017?

8. True or false – There was a distance of more than 20 years before Rossi's first and last podium finishes?

9. Between 2002 and 2004 Rossi reached the podium in how many successive races?

10. True or false – Valentino is a nephew of the World Cup-winning footballer Paolo Rossi?

11. Rossi won his last MotoGP in 2017 at which circuit?

12. Which Italian football team does Rossi famously support?

13. Rossi won his first three World Championships riding a bike made by which manufacturer?

14. Rossi also won multiple World Championships riding bikes made by what other manufacturer?

15. Rossi won which race seven years in a row between 2002 and 2008?

16. In what year did Rossi win his last World MotoGP championship?

17. What was the most races Rossi won during a single MotoGP season?

18. How old was Rossi when he retired from MotoGP racing?

19. Rossi holds the record for the most top-class race starts in the history of the sport with how many? a) 362 b) 372 c) 382

20. How many races did Rossi win in his stellar 500cc/MotoGP career? a) 87 b) 88 c) 89

Quiz 3: Answers

1. Kenny Roberts Sr. and Kenny Roberts Jr. 2. Fédération Internationale de Motocyclisme 3. Switzerland 4. Darryn Binder 5. Eddie Lawson 6. Argentina 7. True 8. Freddie Spencer 9. 20 points 10. Germany 11. Joan Mir 12. One 13. Saturday 14. They're the only left-handed riders 15. Valentino Rossi 16. Stefan Bradl 17. Marc Marquez 18. Six races 19. b) 45 minutes 20. b) Majorca

Quiz 5: Pot Luck

1. Who was the first Spaniard to be crowned World Champion?

2. The German Moto GP is hosted at what circuit?

3. Who was the first Ducati rider to win the MotoGP World Championship?

4. Which country hosted four races during the 2022 MotoGP season?

5. The curve known as "Chemin aux Boeufs" is a feature of which circuit?

6. Which Italian won his first Grand Prix at the 124th time of asking in the 2019 Italian Grand Prix?

7. In what month does the British MotoGP usually take place?

8. In 2016, who became the first British rider in 35 years to win a premier class race?

9. He gained that famous victory in which race?

10. Who was the last British rider before that to have won a premier class race?

11. How many points does the third-place finisher in a MotoGP race receive?

12. Which rider appears on social media using the name @valeyellow46?

13. How many points are awarded to the winner of a MotoGP Sprint Race?

14. True or false – The first edition of the Portuguese Grand Prix was actually hosted in Spain?

15. The Laguna Seca Raceway, which hosted a series of Grand Prix races between 1988 and 2013, is in which US state?

16. Who holds the record for the most wins in the Australian Grand Prix by an Aussie rider?

17. What flag does a marshal wave to indicate that there is oil, gravel, grass or other debris on the track?

18. The fastest speed ever recorded in a MotoGP race was recorded in 2022 by which rider?

19. What was that speed? a) 361.6 km/h b) 362.6 km/h c) 363.6 km/h

20. That record speed was achieved in a race at which circuit? a) Assen b) Mugello c) Silverstone

Quiz 4: Answers

1. Italian 2. Seven 3. True 4. #46 5. Second 6. British Grand Prix 7. Dutch 8. True 9. 23 races 10. False 11. Assen 12. Inter Milan 13. Honda 14. Yamaha 15. Italian GP 16. 2009 17. 11 races 18. 42 years old 19. b) 372 starts 20. c) 89 races

Quiz 6: Marc Marquez

1. Marc Marquez represents which country?

2. Since entering MotoGP, Marquez has been a member of which team?

3. In what year did Marquez win his first MotoGP Championship?

4. Marquez made the podium in his debut MotoGP appearance at which Asian race?

5. During the 2014 season, Marquez won how many races in a row?

6. True or false – Marquez started riding motorbikes at the age of four?

7. What is the name of Marc's brother who is also a MotoGP rider?

8. An image of what insect appears on Marquez's helmet?

9. What is Marquez's number?

10. Marquez suffered a serious injury at the 2020 Spanish Moto GP, breaking which bone?

11. Up to the start of the 2023 season, Marquez had won how many World Championships?

12. Up to the start of the 2023 season, Marquez had won which race the most times?

13. True or false – Marquez is the only rider to make the podium in each of his first four MotoGP starts?

14. Marquez reached the podium for the 100th time in his MotoGP career at which 2022 race?

15. What is the highest number of races Marquez has won in a single MotoGP season?

16. True or false – On racedays, Marquez always wears lucky red underpants?

17. Marquez pipped which Italian to the 2017 title after a tense final round at the Valencian Grand Prix?

18. How old was Marquez when he won his first MotoGP World Championship?

19. What is the lowest position that Marquez has finished in the overall season rankings? a) 12th b) 13th c) 14th

20. Marquez secured his first MotoGP race win in which event? a) GP of the Americas b) French c) Italian

Quiz 5: Answers

1. Àlex Crivillé 2. Sachsenring 3. Casey Stoner 4. Spain 5. Le Mans 6. Danilo Petrucci 7. August 8. Cal Crutchlow 9. Czech Republic MotoGP 10. Barry Sheene 11. 16 points 12. Valentino Rossi 13. 12 points 14. True 15. California 16. Casey Stoner 17. Red and yellow vertical stripes 18. Jorge Martín 19. c) 363.6 km/h 20. b) Mugello

Quiz 7: Pot Luck

1. Who is the only rider to have won the BBC Sports Personality of the Year Award?

2. Which circuit is sometimes known as 'The Cathedral of Motorcycling'?

3. Which Italian's 247 starts between 2008 and 2022 are the second most in the history of MotoGP?

4. What number bike did Casey Stoner ride?

5. Who holds the record for the most Grand Prix wins in a season?

6. Which Venezuelan won three premier class motorcycle Grand Prix races in the 1970s before going on to appear in 23 races as a Formula One driver in the 1980s?

7. Which MotoGP rider was named after a movie character played by Tom Cruise?

8. Which rider secured the first ever premier class race win for Aprilia in the 2022 Argentine MotoGP?

9. How many riders receive points in a MotoGP Sprint race?

10. Up to the start of the 2023 season, only two riders had won Moto2 and the MotoGP World Championships. Which two?

11. At what time (in local time) do MotoGP Grands Prix usually start?

12. What colour flag is waved at a driver to indicate they are about to be passed by a fellow rider?

13. Who is the only British rider to have won the Australian MotoGP?

14. What are quicker – MotoGP bikes or World Superbikes?

15. Up until 2016 MotoGP tyres were supplied by which manufacturer?

16. The fourth-place finisher in a MotoGP race receives how many points?

17. The late Michel Frutschi is the only rider from which country to have won a motorcycle Grand Prix?

18. Johann Zarco and Franco Morbidelli were involved in a spectacular crash at turn three on lap nine of the 2020 edition of which race?

19. Valentino Rossi took part in premier class races at how many different circuits? a) 19 b) 29 c) 39

20. How old was Valentino Rossi when he won his last World Championship? a) 30 b) 32 c) 34

Quiz 6: Answers

1. Spain 2. Repsol Honda Team 3. 2013 4. Qatar Grand Prix 5. Ten 6. True 7. Alex 8. An ant 9. #93 10. Humerus (upper arm) 11. Six 12. German Grand Prix 13. False 14. Australian Grand Prix 15. 13 races 16. True 17. Andrea Dovizioso 18. 20 years old 19. b) 13th 20. a) GP of the Americas

Quiz 8: Anagrams – World Champions

Rearrange the letters to make up the name of a Grand Prix World Champion.

1. Venison Tailors

2. Domino Hack

3. Tony Creases

4. Wines Loaded

5. Enrol Jog Zero

6. Roadside Nap

7. Eraser By Hen

8. Facing Arab Oceans

9. Wine Any Year

10. Wink Cash Zen TV

11. Sentry Broken

12. Energy Rwanda

13. Lexical Liver

14. Uh No Jesters

15. Who Leak Idiom

16. Finder Precedes

17. Ingot Amigos Ciao

18. Iron Jam

19. Orb For Aqua Tiara

20. Feud Of Keg

Quiz 7: Answers

1. John Surtees 2. Assen 3. Andrea Dovizioso 4. #27 5. Marc Marquez 6. Johnny Cecotto 7. Maverick Viñales 8. Aleix Espargaró 9. Nine 10. Marc Marquez and Francesco Bagnaia 11. 2pm 12. Blue 13. Cal Crutchlow 14. MotoGP bikes 15. Bridgestone 16. 13 points 17. Switzerland 18. Austrian Grand Prix 19. b) 29 circuits 20. a) 30

Quiz 9: Pot Luck

1. Which MotoGP is hosted at the KymiRing Circuit?

2. Prior to Francesco Bagnaia, who was the last Italian riding an Italian bike to win the premier class World Championship?

3. In 2021, who became the first Frenchman to be crowned World Champion?

4. He won the title riding what manufacturer's bike?

5. Who was the first rider to win 10 races in a single season?

6. Which American appeared in 196 races between 2003 and 2014 but didn't win any of them?

7. Which Asian race returned to the MotoGP calendar for the first time in 24 years in 2022?

8. How many points are awarded to the fifth-place finisher in a MotoGP race?

9. Excluding the Covid-interrupted 2020 season, what are the two Grand Prix races to have taken place every year since the competition began?

10. China hosted a motorcycle Grand Prix from 2005 to 2008. In which city did it take place?

11. Which city in Midwest America hosted a Grand Prix from 2008 until 2015?

12. How many riders start each MotoGP race?

13. 'Pushing the Limits' was the title of which multiple World Champion's 2014 autobiography?

14. What nickname is shared by an Italian rider on the 2023 grid and a member of hedonistic Manchester indie rockers the Happy Mondays?

15. Which rider finished third in the BBC Sports Personality of the Year Award in 1977?

16. 'Pecco' is the nickname of which rider?

17. The runner-up finisher in a MotoGP Sprint race receives how many points?

18. Franta Statsny is the only rider from which country to have won a motorcycle Grand Prix?

19. The 2020 season tied a record after how many different riders won a Grand Prix? a) eight b) nine c) ten

20. Kevin Schwantz was the last rider to ride what number bike? a) #34 b) #35 c) #36

Quiz 8: Answers

1. Valentino Rossi 2. Mick Doohan 3. Casey Stoner 4. Eddie Lawson 5. Jorge Lorenzo 6. Dani Pedrosa 7. Barry Sheene 8. Francesco Bagnaia 9. Wayne Rainey 10. Kevin Schwantz 11. Kenny Roberts 12. Wayne Gardner 13. Alex Criville 14. John Surtees 15. Mike Hailwood 16. Freddie Spencer 17. Giacomo Agostini 18. Joan Mir 19. Fabio Quartararo 20. Geoff Duke

Quiz 10: Legends

1. Who are the three riders to have been crowned World Champion five seasons in a row?

2. Who was the first rider to break the 400-point barrier in a single season?

3. Who are the two riders to have won all the races of a single Grand Prix season?

4. Between 1986 and 1988 which Aussie became the first rider to make the points in 30 successive races?

5. Who holds the record for starting the season with the most podium appearances?

6. Which Californian star earned two sixth place finishes in the IndyCar series following his retirement from motorcycle racing?

7. Which legend almost drowned after jumping into a lake following a stunning race win in Jerez in 2010?

8. Which 19-year-old American became the youngest rider to reach the podium in a 1979 race in Finland?

9. Which Aussie won his home Grand Prix every year between 2007 and 2012?

10. Who holds the record for winning the most points in the history of Grand Prix racing?

11. Who is second on that all-time points list?

12. Which Australian legend was associated with a moto-themed roller coaster at a Queensland theme park?

13. Who holds the record for the most career pole positions?

14. Who is the only rider to gain pole in 12 consecutive races?

15. Who holds the record for the most runner-up finishes in the history of Grand Prix racing?

16. Who was the first American to be crowned World Champion more than once?

17. Who is the only rider to win the World Championship seven seasons in a row?

18. Who has earned the most points in the history of Grand Prix racing without ever being crowned World Champion?

19. Valentino Rossi made the podium in how many successive seasons? a) 19 b) 20 c) 21

20. Of riders with at least 15 starts, who has the best win percentage? a) Giacomo Agostini b) Mick Doohan c) John Surtees

Quiz 9: Answers

1. Finnish 2. Giacomo Agostini 3. Fabio Quartararo 4. Yamaha 5. Giacomo Agostini 6. Colin Edwards 7. Indonesia MotoGP 8. 11 points 9. Dutch TT and Italian Grand Prix 10. Shanghai 11. Indianapolis 12. 24 riders 13. Casey Stoner 14. Bez 15. Barry Sheene 16. Francesco Bagnaia 17. Nine 18. Czechia 19. b) Nine 20. a) #34

Quiz 11: Pot Luck

1. Who holds the record for the most Grand Prix wins by a British rider?

2. Who was the first rider to win the World Championship riding a Japanese bike?

3. Who is the youngest rider to have been crowned MotoGP World Champion?

4. In 1997, which Australian became the first rider to win 11 races in a single season?

5. Who was the only Australian to win a race throughout the whole of the 2022 MotoGP season?

6. Who was runner-up in the World Championship standings in 2017, 2018 and 2019?

7. What colour flag is waved to bring the race to an immediate halt?

8. Who was the only rider to feature during the 2022 season whose full name starts and ends with the same letter?

9. The Paul Ricard Circuit, which has hosted 13 motorcycle Grands Prix, is in which country?

10. 'Dreams Come True: My Story' was the title of which multiple World Champion's 2014 autobiography?

11. Who were the two Americans to be crowned World Champion during the 2000s?

12. Who holds the record for the most MotoGP wins riding a Ducati?

13. Which British rider made nine podium finishes between 1983 and 1987 but never won a race?

14. Since the inception of the MotoGP brand, which team has won the World Team Championship the most times?

15. The rider finishing in sixth place in a MotoGP receives how many points?

16. Marc Marquez won which race eight times in a row from 2013 to 2021?

17. Which Briton made the points in 26 straight races between 2014 and 2016?

18. The San Marino and Rimini Riviera MotoGP is hosted at which circuit?

19. Up to the end of the 2022 season, how many different countries had hosted a motorcycle Grand Prix? a) 25 b) 27 c) 29

20. How many times did Valentino Rossi make the podium during his stellar career? a) 179 b) 189 c) 199

Quiz 10: Answers

1. Giacomo Agostini, Mick Doohan and Valentino Rossi 2. Marc Marquez 3. John Surtees and Giacomo Agostini 4. Wayne Gardner 5. Valentino Rossi 6. Eddie Lawson 7. Jorge Lorenzo 8. Randy Mamola 9. Casey Stoner 10. Valentino Rossi 11. Dani Pedrosa 12. Mick Doohan 13. Marc Marquez 14. Mick Doohan 15. Valentino Rossi 16. Kenny Roberts Sr. 17. Giacomo Agostini 18. Dani Pedrosa 19. c) 21 seasons 20. c) John Surtees

Quiz 12: Firsts, Lasts and Onlys

1. In what year did the first motorcycle Grand Prix take place?

2. At which famous location was the inaugural race held?

3. Which Briton was crowned motorcycling's first World Champion?

4. The first MotoGP race staged at night was hosted in which country?

5. What was the first Japanese manufacturer to win a premier class Grand Prix?

6. Which Briton became the first rider to win three World Championships in a row in 1953, 1954 and 1955?

7. The first race of a new MotoGP season usually takes place in which month?

8. Which American won his first and only MotoGP World Championship in 2006?

9. Who was the first rider not representing Britain or Italy to be crowned World Champion?

10. Who was the only World Champion crowned between 1975 and 2021 who didn't win the title riding a Japanese bike?

11. The first Grand Prix Motorcycle race hosted in Asia was held in 1963 in which country?

12. Which two countries were added to the MotoGP calendar for the first time in 2023?

13. Prior to Fabio Quartararo, who was the last non-Spaniard to be crowned MotoGP Champion?

14. The first World Championship race held outside of Europe was hosted in what country?

15. Who was the last American rider to win multiple premier class World Championships?

16. In what year was a British rider last crowned World Champion?

17. Which Spanish rider secured his first MotoGP win at the 200th attempt at the 2022 Argentine Grand Prix?

18. Which World Superbikes champ secured his first and last MotoGP race win at the 2006 Valencian Grand Prix?

19. Who is the only Australian to have won the World Championship just once? a) Mick Doohan b) Wayne Gardner c) Casey Stoner

20. Francesco Bagnaia secured his first World Championship in the last race of the 2022 season at which Grand Prix? a) Australian b) Malaysian c) Valencian

Quiz 11: Answers

1. Mike Hailwood 2. Giacomo Agostini 3. Marc Marquez 4. Mick Doohan 5. Jack Miller 6. Andrea Dovizioso 7. Red 8. Remy Gardner 9. France 10. Marc Marquez 11. Kenny Roberts Jr. and Nicky Hayden 12. Casey Stoner 13. Ron Haslam 14. Repsol Honda 15. 10 points 16. German Grand Prix 17. Bradley Smith 18. Misano World Circuit Marco Simoncelli 19. c) 29 countries 20. c) 199 times

Quiz 13: Pot Luck

1. Who is the only man to have been crowned a World Champion on motorbikes and in Formula One?

2. Up to the start of the 2023 season Francesco Bagnaia rode what number bike?

3. The Mobility Resort Motegi is in which country?

4. Who holds the record for the most MotoGP race wins by a Spanish rider?

5. Which rider has the most race wins but has never won the World Championship?

6. Who are the two riders to have finished in the points more than 200 times?

7. True or false – The character Jorge in the video game 'Halo: Reach' is named after Jorge Lorenzo?

8. Who finished second in the World Championship standings in 2007, 2010 and 2012?

9. The third placed finisher in a MotoGP Sprint race is awarded how many points?

10. What colour flag is waved to declare a 'wet race', allowing riders to return to the pits and switch to a new bike?

11. What is the only African country to have hosted a motorcycle Grand Prix?

12. With five victories between 2009 and 2016 who is the most successful rider in the history of the French Grand Prix?

13. Which Grand Prix, which ran twice in the 1990s, was hosted at the Sentul International Circuit?

14. 'Feel' was the title of the 2017 autobiography of which American World Champion?

15. Prior to Jack Miller who was the last Australian to claim a MotoGP pole?

16. Barry Sheene was one of two British riders to be crowned World Champion in the 1970s. Who was the other?

17. Which Spanish rider won back-to-back MotoE World Championships in 2020 and 2021?

18. Barry Sheene famously rode what number bike?

19. Across the 1968 and 1969 seasons Giacomo Agostini won how many consecutive races? a) 18 b) 19 c) 20

20. The Circuit Ricordo Tormo is in which Spanish city? a) Barcelona b) Madrid c) Valencia

Quiz 12: Answers

1. 1949 2. Isle of Man 3. Leslie Graham 4. Qatar 5. Honda 6. Geoff Duke 7. March 8. Nicky Hayden 9. Gary Hocking 10. Casey Stoner 11. Japan 12. India and Kazakhstan 13. Casey Stoner 14. Argentina 15. Wayne Rainey 16. 1977 17. Aleix Espargaró 18. Troy Bayliss 19. b) Wayne Gardner 20. c) Valencian

Quiz 14: Current Riders

1. Whose 2021 rookie campaign included four pole positions, a win in the Styrian Grand Prix and a ninth-place finish in the championship standings?

2. Which member of the 2023 grid has a degree in dentistry?

3. True or false – Brad Binder represented South Africa at cricket as a junior?

4. In 2015 who became the first rider to make the jump directly from Moto3 to MotoGP?

5. Which rider is known for celebrating victory with a backflip?

6. Which of the two Espargaro brothers is older – Pol or Aleix?

7. Who was the only rookie to join the MotoGP lineup for the start of the 2023 season?

8. Which dapper dresser has modelled for the Italian fashion house Dolce & Gabbana?

9. Who was the oldest rider to appear in a MotoGP race during the 2022 season?

10. True or false – Former champion Joan Mir does not have a road motorbike licence?

11. Which future World Champion won the 2017 Moto3 Championship?

12. Which current rider is the half-brother of MotoGP legend Valentino Rossi?

13. True or false – Franco Morbidelli is the son of former Formula One driver Gianni Morbidelli?

14. Who is the only rider to win races in all three classes at the Circuit of the Americas?

15. Which Mooney VR46 rider gained one pole and one podium during his 2022 rookie season?

16. Which Spanish rider secured his maiden MotoGP victory at the 2016 British Grand Prix?

17. Who was the first graduate of Valentino Rossi's VR46 Academy to go on to win the MotoGP World Championship?

18. At 184cm (just over 6ft), who is the tallest current MotoGP rider?

19. Who was the highest-placed non-European in the 2022 MotoGP Standings? a) Brad Binder b) Jack Miller c) Takaaki Nagakami

20. Miguel Oliveira is the first MotoGP winner from which country? a) Brazil b) Mexico c) Portugal

Quiz 13: Answers

1. John Surtees 2. #63 3. Japan 4. Marc Marquez 5. Dani Pedrosa 6. Valentino Rossi and Andrea Dovizioso 7. True 8. Dani Pedrosa 9. Seven points 10. White 11. South Africa 12. Jorge Lorenzo 13. Indonesian 14. Freddie Spencer 15. Casey Stoner 16. Phil Read 17. Jordi Torres 18. #7 19. c) 20 races 20. c) Valencia

Quiz 15: Pot Luck

1. Who holds the record for the most Grand Prix wins by an Australian rider?

2. The Lusail International Circuit is located in which country?

3. Who was the last rider before Marc Marquez to be crowned premier class World Champion in his rookie season?

4. In 1985, which American became the first rider to make pole 10 times in a single season?

5. At 5.9km long, what was the longest circuit on the 2022 MotoGP calendar?

6. True or false – The grid positions for the Sprint and main MotoGP race are the same?

7. What flag is waved at a rider to tell him their race is over and they must return to the pit lane?

8. True or false – Stefan Bradl is the son of 1990s 250cc specialist Helmut Bradl?

9. Which circuit has hosted the most motorcycle Grand Prix races?

10. What are the three South American countries to have hosted a motorcycle Grand Prix?

11. Sun and the moon motifs regularly appeared on the helmet worn by which rider?

12. The short-lived Pacific Grand Prix, which ran from 2000 to 2003 was hosted in which country?

13. How many points are awarded to the seventh-place finisher in a MotoGP race?

14. Who holds the record for the most wins in the Portuguese Grand Prix?

15. Marc Marquez pipped Fabio Quartararo to victory on the final corner of the 2019 edition of which Asian Grand Prix?

16. Which rider was tragically killed at the 2011 Malaysian Grand Prix?

17. Which manufacturer replaced Energica as the sole bike supplier for the 2023 MotoE World Cup?

18. Since 1999 the Malaysian Grand Prix has been hosted at which track?

19. Marc Marquez won the 2019 World Championship with a record haul of how many points? a) 410 b) 420 c) 430

20. Cal Crutchlow is from which English midland city? a) Coventry b) Derby c) Leicester

Quiz 14: Answers

1. Jorge Martin 2. Miguel Oliveira 3. False 4. Jack Miller 5. Johann Zarco 6. Aleix 7. Augusto Fernandez 8. Fabio Quartararo 9. Andrea Dovizioso 10. True 11. Joan Mir 12. Luca Marini 13. False 14. Alex Rins 15. Marco Bezzecchi 16. Maverick Viñales 17. Francesco Bagnaia 18. Luca Marini 19. b) Jack Miller 20. c) Portugal

Quiz 16: Memorable Moments

1. Who secured his only World Riders' Championship after a third-place finish in an epic 2006 Valencian MotoGP?

2. In 2003, who became the first rider to win a MotoGP race riding a Ducati?

3. Which Briton was the first rider to win 10 motorcycle Grand Prix races in a row?

4. Who won the 2015 World Championship despite not making the podium in any of his first three races?

5. In 1975, which two all-time greats were given exactly the same time after a photo finish?

6. That memorable finish happened at which race?

7. Who executed a spectacular pass on the final turn to win the 2009 Catalan MotoGP by just by 0.09 seconds?

8. Which great rival finished second in that famous Barcelona finale?

9. Which 20-year-old great secured his first MotoGP victory at the 2006 Chinese Grand Prix?

10. Which rider was given a 10-second penalty during a 2003 MotoGP but still went on to comfortably win the race?

11. That spectacular comeback victory happened at which race?

12. Casey Stoner secured his first race victory in 2007 in which MotoGP?

13. Which British rider has enjoyed podium finishes in MotoGP, Moto2, 125cc World Championship and MotoE races?

14. In what year did Ducati secure their first triple crown of rider, constructor and team titles?

15. In 1977, which rider set the record for the fastest average speed in a motorcycle Grand Prix?

16. He set that record at which former circuit which is now much better known as a Formula One venue?

17. Which former champ retired from competitive motorbike racing in 2012, aged just 27?

18. Which constructor has won the most Constructors' Championship titles?

19. The 2004 Motorcycle Grand Prix was the shortest in history. How long was it? a) 29.47km b) 31.47km c) 33.47km

20. What is the record number of points between the first and second-place finishers in the MotoGP Riders' Championship? a) 131 b) 141 c) 151

Quiz 15: Answers

1. Mick Doohan 2. Qatar 3. Kenny Roberts Sr. 4. Freddie Spencer 5. Silverstone 6. True 7. Black 8. True 9. Assen TT 10. Argentina, Brazil and Venezuela 11. Valentino Rossi 12. Japan 13. Nine 14. Valentino Rossi 15. Thai MotoGP 16. Marco Simoncelli 17. Ducati 18. Sepang International Circuit 19. b) 420 points 20. a) Coventry

Quiz 17: Pot Luck

1. With 31 Grand Prix wins, who is the most successful American rider of all-time?

2. The Mandalika International Street Circuit is in which country?

3. Which Spaniard crashed just twice during the 2022 MotoGP season, the fewest times of any rider that year?

4. Who is the youngest rider to have won a MotoGP race?

5. Eight points are awarded to the rider that finishes in which position in a MotoGP race?

6. At what time (in local time) do MotoGP Sprint races take place?

7. True or false – Francesco Bagnaia won the 2022 World Championship despite failing to finish a record five races?

8. Who became the youngest rider to gain pole in a MotoGP at the 2019 French Grand Prix?

9. What colour is the circle on the black flag that shows a rider there is a technical problem with their bike?

10. True or false – Johann Zarco is a trained chiropractor?

11. Which American holds the record for the most wins in the Japanese Grand Prix?

12. Which rider gave KTM Tech3 their first MotoGP victory in 373 premier class starts at the 2020 Styrian Grand Prix?

13. Which Japanese rider won his first World Championship points in 1989 and his last 22 years later in 2011?

14. Which British rider won the Ulster GP in 1964 then had to wait until the 1973 German Grand Prix for his next victory?

15. Which Grand Prix was hosted at the Phakisa Freeway between 1999 and 2004?

16. 'Fast Freddie' was the nickname of which popular American?

17. Before Francesco Bagnaia in 2023, who was the last rider to defend his World Championship while riding a bike with the #1 plate?

18. The Red Bull Ring circuit is in which country?

19. Giacomo Agostini won which race nine times in a row during the 60s and 70s? a) Dutch TT b) Finnish c) Italian

20. Valentino Rossi started the 2003 season by making the podium in how many consecutive races? a) 15 b) 16 c) 17

Quiz 16: Answers

1. Nicky Hayden 2. Loris Capirossi 3. John Surtees 4. Jorge Lorenzo 5. Barry Sheene and Giacomo Agostino 6. Dutch TT 7. Valentino Rossi 8. Jorge Lorenzo 9. Dani Pedrosa 10. Valentino Rossi 11. Australian MotoGP 12. Qatar GP 13. Bradley Smith 14. 2022 15. Barry Sheene 16. Spa Francorchamps 17. Casey Stoner 18. Honda 19. b) 31.47km 20. c) 151 points

Quiz 18: Moto2

1. Which Spaniard won the 2022 Moto2 Championship?

2. Which future MotoGP World Champion won the 2012 Moto2 Championship?

3. Which Briton was crowned 2020 Moto2 Champion?

4. Which three constructors had bikes in the 2022 Moto2 competition?

5. Who holds the record for the most Moto2 race wins?

6. Which British rider made the podium six times during the 2022 season?

7. In 2022, Somkiat Chantra became the first rider from which country to win a Moto2 race?

8. All Moto2 engines are provided by which manufacturer?

9. Who is the only rider to have won the Moto2 Championship more than once?

10. Which country has produced the most race winners in the history of the Moto2 competition?

11. Who became the first American to win a Moto2 race at the 2022 Grand Prix of Portugal?

12. In what year was the Moto2 class introduced?

13. Which Spaniard was the winner of that inaugural competition?

14. The champion Moto2 constructor Ajo is based in which Nordic country?

15. Which country hosted the first ever Moto2 race?

16. Who is the only German to have won the Moto2 Championship?

17. Which Japanese rider won three races during the 2022 Moto2 season?

18. Xavier Simon is the only rider from which country to have won a Moto2 race?

19. What size is the engine in the Moto2 competition? a) 705cc b) 735cc c) 765cc

20. What is the minimum combined bike/rider weight in Moto2 races? a) 207kg b) 217kg c) 227kg

Quiz 17: Answers

1. Eddie Lawson 2. Indonesia 3. Maverick Viñales 4. Marc Marquez 5. Eighth 6. 3pm 7. True 8. Fabio Quartararo 9. Orange 10. False – but his brother is 11. Kevin Schwantz 12. Miguel Oliveira 13. Shinichi Ito 14. Phil Read 15. South African 16. Freddie Spencer 17. Casey Stoner 18. Austria 19. b) Finnish 20. b) 16 races

Quiz 19: Pot Luck

1. Why is Harold Daniell an important name in the history of the sport?

2. From 2010 onwards the British MotoGP has been hosted at which circuit?

3. Who holds the record for the most premier class World Championships by an Australian rider?

4. The Imatra Circuit was the former home of Grand Prix races in which country?

5. Which 21-year-old secured his maiden race victory at the 2020 Spanish Grand Prix?

6. True or false – Valentino Rossi is a fan of rallying and has twice taken part in the British leg of the World Rally Championship?

7. Which Aussie is the oldest rider to have gained pole position in a Grand Prix?

8. Which rider made his debut in 1986 but didn't win a World Championship until 1993?

9. The Autódromo Termas de Río Hondo is in which country?

10. Who was the only British rider to appear in a race during the 2022 MotoGP season?

11. At 3.7km, what is the shortest circuit on the MotoGP calendar?

12. Up to 2015 the Dutch TT race took place on what day of the week?

13. True or false – As a youngster, Barry Sheene appeared alongside legendary singer Maria Callas in a performance at the Royal Opera House?

14. Who were the two Italians to be crowned World Champion during the 1980s?

15. Which Italian rider was the focus of a TV documentary called 'Undaunted'?

16. Bike manufacturer KTM is based in which country?

17. Which rider has ridden on bikes with the numbers #48, #1 and #99?

18. Who holds the record for the most victories in the Dutch TT?

19. In 1967, which country hosted its one and only motorcycle Grand Prix? a) Canada b) Mexico c) New Zealand

20. In 2019, Marc Marquez set a record after making how many podiums during the 19-race season? a) 16 b) 17 c) 18

Quiz 18: Answers

1. Augusto Fernandez 2. Marc Marquez 3. Sam Lowes 4. Kalex, Boscoscuro and MV Agusta 5. Marc Marquez 6. Jake Dixon 7. Thailand 8. Triumph 9. Johann Zarco 10. Spain 11. Joe Roberts 12. 2010 13. Toni Elias 14. Finland 15. Qatar 16. Stefan Bradl 17. Ai Ogura 18. Belgium 19. a) 765cc 20. b) 217kg

Quiz 20: Nicknames

Match the nickname to the rider.

1. Doctor	a) Fabio Quartoraro
2. The Martian	b) Mick Doohan
3. Ant of Cervana	c) Jorge Lorenzo
4. El Diablo	d) Giacomo Agostini
5. Top Gun	e) Jorge Martin
6. X-Fuera	f) Eddie Lawson
7. Einstein	g) Valentino Rossi
8. Careless Chucker	h) Nicky Hayden
9. Dead By June	i) John Surtees
10. Roman Emperor	j) Miguel Oliveira
11. Ago	k) Dani Pedrosa
12. The Beast	l) Kenny Roberts
13. Martinator	m) Wayne Gardner
14. Thriller	n) Carlos Checa
15. Samurai	o) Barry Sheene
16. Steady	p) Marc Marquez
17. Son of the Wind	q) Enea Bastianini

18. The Bionic Man   r) Max Biaggi

19. Wollongong Whiz   s) Jack Miller

20. The Kentucky Kid   t) Maverick Viñales

Quiz 19: Answers

1. He won the first ever motorcycle Grand Prix 2. Silverstone 3. Mick Doohan 4. Finland 5. Fabio Quartararo 6. True 7. Jack Findlay 8. Kevin Schwantz 9. Argentina 10. Cal Crutchlow 11. Sachsenring 12. Saturday 13. True 14. Marco Lucchinelli and Franco Uncini 15. Andrea Dovizioso 16. Austria 17. Jorge Lorenzo 18. Valentino Rossi 19. a) Canada 20. c) 18

Quiz 21: Pot Luck

1. With seven victories, who is Brazil's most successful Grand Prix motorcyclist?

2. The Circuit of the Americas is located in which US state?

3. True or false – At one stage during the 2022 season, eventual winner Francesco Bagnaia was 91 points behind the then competition leader?

4. Who was the first Spaniard to win the World Championship in back-to-back seasons?

5. Which legendary rider holds the record for making the points in the most consecutive races?

6. Which rider won at least one MotoGP race every year between 2006 and 2017?

7. The Mugello Circuit is owned by which Italian car giant?

8. Three points are awarded to the rider who crosses the finish line in what position in a MotoGP race?

9. Which current MotoGP star was the first winner of the Red Bull Rookies Cup way back in 2007?

10. The first British Motorcycle Grand Prix to take place on the British mainland was hosted at which circuit?

11. Who were the four riders to appear in a race during the 2022 season whose first name and surname star with the same letter?

12. Who won eight races during the 2013 season but still didn't win the World Championship?

13. Excluding Japanese firms, which constructor has been responsible for the most race wins in the history of motorcycle Grand Prix racing?

14. Maggots and Becketts are curves at which circuit?

15. Who was the first South African to win a premier class Grand Prix?

16. Which constructor won their first Riders' Championship since 2000 courtesy of Joan Mir?

17. The 11th place finisher in a MotoGP is awarded how many points?

18. Which American World Champion rode a bike with the #19 plate?

19. MotoGP bikes generates approximately how much horse power? a) 250BHP b) 275BHP c) 300BHP

20. What is the minimum weight of a MotoGP bike? a) 147kg b) 157kg c) 167kg

Quiz 20: Answers

1. G) Valentino Rossi 2. L) Kenny Roberts 3. P) Marc Marquez 4. A) Fabio Quartoraro 5. T) Maverick Viñales 6. C) Jorge Lorenzo 7. J) Miguel Oliveira 8. N) Carlos Checa 9. B) Mick Doohan 10. R) Max Biaggi 11. D) Giacomo Agostini 12. Q) Enea Bastianini 13. E) Jorge Martin 14. S) Jack Miller 15. K) Dani Pedrosa 16. F) Steady 17. I) John Surtees 18. O) Barry Sheene 19. M) Wayne Gardner 20. H) Nicky Hayden

Quiz 22: Numbers Game

Match the rider to the 2023 plate number.

1. Johann Zarco   a) #36

2. Enea Bastianini   b) #42

3. Jack Miller   c) #20

4. Joan Mir   d) #88

5. Jorge Martin   e) #76

6. Marc Marquez   f) #30

7. Fabio Quartararo   g) #44

8. Brad Binder   h) #12

9. Maverick Viñales   i) #5

10. Marco Bezzecchi   j) #89

11. Aleix Espargaro   k) #73

12. Pol Espargaro   l) #10

13. Miguel Oliveira   m) #23

14. Alex Marquez   n) #49

15. Alex Rins   o) #41

16. Franco Morbidelli   p) #33

17. Luca Marini   q) #1

18. Takaaki Nakagami   r) #21

19. Fabio Di Giannantonio   s) #43

20. Francesco Bagnaia   t) #93

Quiz 21: Answers

1. Alex Barros 2. Texas 3. True 4. Marc Marquez 5. Mick Doohan 6. Dani Pedrosa 7. Ferrari 8. 13th 9. Johann Zarco 10. Silverstone 11. Brad Binder, Marc Marquez, Cal Crutchlow and Takuya Tsuda 12. Jorge Lorenzo 13. MV Agusta 14. Silverstone 15. Brad Binder 16. Suzuki 17. Five 18. Freddie Spencer 19. c) 300BHP 20. b) 157kg

Quiz 23: Pot Luck

1. Who was the last Briton to win the World Championship?

2. Which drink became the official sponsor of the British MotoGP in 2021?

3. Who is the only rider to win a MotoGP and a World Superbikes race in the same season?

4. Who is the only American rider to have won a premier class race in seven successive seasons?

5. Which South American was the first rider to start 150 premier class races in a row?

6. Who holds the record for the most third-place finishes in the history of Grand Prix racing?

7. In what decade did MotoGP bikes move from leaded to unleaded fuel?

8. The Circuito de Jerez in Spain is named after which Spanish rider?

9. True or false – Remy Gardner is the son of former 500cc World Champion Wayne Gardner?

10. Which country has hosted the most Grand Prix races in the history of the championship?

11. #69 was the bike number of which American World Champion?

12. 'What if I Had Never Tried It' was the title of which World Champion's 2006 autobiography?

13. Who was the last rider to win the Riders' World Championship with two different constructors?

14. Who was the only World Champion from the 1990s who wasn't an American or Australian?

15. True or false – Raul and Augusto Fernandez are brothers?

16. The Chang International Circuit is located on which country?

17. In 1982, who became the first woman to compete in a premier class motorcycle Grand Prix?

18. 'Rocket' was the nickname of which British rider from the 1980s?

19. On the MotoGP grid, riders are separated from each other by what distance? a) 8 metres b) 9 metres c) 10 metres

20. The Phillip Island Circuit is in which Australian state? a) New South Wales b) Queensland c) Victoria

Quiz 22: Answers

1. Johan Zarco i) #5 2. Enea Bastianini m) #23 3. Jack Miller s) #43 4. Joan Mir a) #36 5. Jorge Martin j) #89 6. Marc Marquez t) #93 7. Fabio Quartararo c) #20 8. Brad Binder p) #33 9. Maverick Viñales h) #12 10. Marco Bezzecchi e) #76 11. Aleix Espargaro o) #41 12. Pol Espargaro g) #44 13. Miguel Oliveira d) #88 14. Alex Marquez k) #73 15. Alex Rins b) #42 16. Franco Morbidelli r) #21 17. Luca Marini l) #10 18. Takaaki Nakagami f) #30 19. Fabio Di Giannantonio n) #49 20. Francesco Bagnaia q) #1

Quiz 24: Anagrams (Current Riders)

Rearrange the letters to make the name of a current rider.

1. Barb Ridden

2. Learn Six

3. Karmic Jell

4. John On Λ Czar

5. Join Mr Great

6. Nae Insane Tibia

7. Evil Irks Caveman

8. Grave Oil Milieu

9. Gear Proposal

10. Axial Grease Pro

11. Claim A Ruin

12. Braced For Million

13. Fun Zone Graduates

14. Catch Curl Owl

15. Merry Danger

16. Include Apricot

17. Darn Belfast

18. Aaron Divides Zoo

19. Cabin Carnage Oafs

20. Dr Barny Diner

Quiz 23: Answers

1. Barry Sheene 2. Monster 3. Troy Bayliss 4. Kevin Schwantz 5. Alex Barros 6. Valentino Rossi 7. 1990s 8. Angel Nieto 9. True 10. Spain 11. Nicky Hayden 12. Valentino Rossi 13. Casey Stoner 14. Àlex Crivillé 15. False 16. Thailand 17. Gina Bovaird 18. Ron Haslam 19. b) 9 metres 20. c) Victoria

Quiz 25: Pot Luck

1. Who was the first American to be crowned World Champion?

2. Which Frenchman set the record for the fastest lap at Silverstone during qualifying for the 2022 British MotoGP?

3. Who are the two Ducati riders with seven or more race wins in a single season?

4. In 1998, who became the first rider to make the podium in each of his first four premier class appearances?

5. Which race was hosted at the Eastern Creek Circuit from 1991 through to 1996?

6. Who is the only World Champion whose surname starts and ends with the same letter?

7. Is the British Grand Prix at Silverstone run in a clockwise or anticlockwise direction?

8. How many points does the 14th place finisher receive in a MotoGP race?

9. Finland is one of two Nordic countries to have hosted a motorcycle Grand Prix. What is the other?

10. What are quicker – MotoGP bikes or Formula One cars?

11. The Styrian Grand Prix, which ran in 2020 and 2021 took place in which country?

12. True or false – On the French equivalent of Top Gear, Johann Zarco beat 'Le Tone' aka 'The Stig' in the fast lap challenge?

13. In a MotoGP race, each row of the grid is made up of how many riders?

14. Who holds the record for winning a race in the highest number of different countries?

15. Global Jet International, a company that provides private aviation services, was founded and operated by which multiple World Champion?

16. Who was the only non-Spaniard to be crowned World Champion during the 2010s?

17. 'Unlimited' was the title of a 2020 documentary about which rider?

18. Between 2000 and 2012 the Portuguese Grand Prix was hosted at which circuit which is better known as a Formula One venue?

19. The amount of fuel a bike can carry in a MotoGP race is capped at how many litres? a) 22 b) 24 c) 26

20. The Mugello Circuit is in which Italian city? a) Florence b) Milan c) Rome

Quiz 24: Answers

1. Brad Binder 2. Alex Rins 3. Jack Miller 4. Johann Zarco 5. Jorge Martin 6. Enea Bastianini 7. Maverick Vinales 8. Miguel Oliveira 9. Pol Espargaro 10. Aleix Espargaro 11. Luca Marini 12. Franco Morbidelli 13. Augusto Fernandez 14. Cal Crutchlow 15. Remy Gardner 16. Danilo Petrucci 17. Stefan Bradl 18. Andrea Dovizioso 19. Franceso Bagnaia 20. Darryn Binder

Formula One Trivia Quiz Book

500 Questions on Grand Prix Greats

ISBN: 173921370X

Printed in Great Britain
by Amazon

34703655R00037